Mind, Body and Spirit:
Complete Health and Well-being with Tai Chi

Donald Kerr

Published by Jeremy Mills Publishing Limited,
The Red House, 22 Occupation Road, Lindley,
Huddersfield HD3 3BD, UK

www.jeremymillspublishing.co.uk

First Published 2006

Text and Images © Donald Kerr 2006

ISBN 978–1–905217–12–0

Typesetting & Book Design by Paul Buckley
Production Editor: Michelle I'Anson

Printed by Replika Press Pt Ltd

Mind, Body and Spirit:
Complete Health and Well-being with Tai Chi

Donald Kerr

"It only takes five minutes to do the form, but I
always feel much better for it".
JANE BELLAMY

"I used to get quite sluggish at work by mid afternoon. Doing
the short form never fails to boost my energy".
SHEENA WATLAL

"I am amazed that a simple set of stretching and breathing
exercises can make me feel so much better".
TAMARA HALL

"I would recommend this to anyone who is too lazy to
join a gym but wants to do a bit of exercise".
CLARE EVANS

"As a working mother I don't get much time to
myself, so this short form is ideal".
CHRISTINA BAKER

"My job can be stressful sometimes and I've found that taking
a short break and doing the form helps to calm me down".
BARRY SHAW

This book is dedicated to my son, who is a constant
source of love and light in my world.

Contents

Foreword

Sport was something that took its time to sit well with me but with the patient teachings of my school P.E. teacher, Mr Tony Scott, I found an outlet for my energies and took to pole vault with great enthusiasm, achieving some considerable success. It gave me the drive to find a way to succeed, applying myself as best I could to achieve my aims and gave me a sense of myself. By the time I began to study Tai Chi and then soon after Chinese medicine, I had reached the conclusion that it was time to think ahead for my future.

Tai Chi, for me, was a martial art that had more to offer than met the eye. Through the opening of my mind and the secrets that were revealed to me by way of Tai Chi it has become so much more. Another pleasure has been meeting a number of inspirational practitioners of the art such as Sifu Peter Young whose ability with the Chan Ssu Chin is impressive to watch.

To study Tai Chi Chuan, whether it is for its health or for its martial aspects, is to begin a journey of self-discovery. My own early impressions of Tai Chi Chuan turned out to be very wrong. The images of Tai Chi as soft and slow were shattered when I started collecting bruises from the martial training.

I remember asking my Sifu, 'What happened to Tai Chi being soft and slow'? – 'It is' he replied 'But not as a martial art'. This was going to be a long, and sometimes (often) painful, road. Through the years the training became harder, more exciting, more painful, more involved but always more rewarding.

I have great respect for my teacher, Raymond Rand, whose skill in Tai Chi Chuan is matched by his skill in teaching. Over the years I have come to know him not only as a Sifu but also as a friend. I have learned through the respect he has for his own Sifu, Master Lam Kam Chuen, to know and understand what it is to be able to appreciate and respect others for their skill. I have been greatly inspired not only by my Sifu and his own training when he began but also by the stories of his Sifu and the many legends told of the old Masters.

I only hope I can inspire my students to aspire to attain great skill also. It is only through the enduring patience and willingness to teach that these arts have been passed down throughout the centuries, through people like my Sifu and Master Lam, people skilled not only in their art but also the more elusive art of teaching.

I developed the Yongquan form through a desire to understand the principal movements and motion of the long form. This led to the discovery of a form that though short, contained all that was needed to exercise and attain good health through the medium of Tai Chi Chuan. This miniature health form obeys all the principles of Tai Chi Chuan but has little emphasis on the Chuan aspects. No longer will those interested in health be required to spend months learning long forms that require many long hours of practice and plenty of space. It was actually my Tai Chi brothers and my Sifu who saw the great potential of this form and in fact began teaching it before I did. It was only once I saw how easily students took to learning this form and how easy it was for them to then move on to the longer forms that I realised for myself how useful it truly was.

Within the Tai Chi community there has been much debate on the use of the term Tai Chi for those who practice the art purely for health. Strictly speaking the term Tai Chi is the proper name for the Yin and Yang symbol we see commonly today. So for the traditionalist to study Tai Chi Chuan for only its health aspects is not to truly study Tai Chi Chuan. I can only convey my thoughts on the matter by comparing an everyday car driver with that of a formula one racing driver. Both are legitimately called drivers, but whilst one has taken the art to its limit the other has only gone as far as they have found necessary to achieve their aims.

It is likely that there have always been those who have practised Tai Chi Chuan for its health gains rather than for its martial skills. In fact, Tai Chi Chuan is probably the most widely practised art in the world but only a small percentage of those people do so for the martial art. For me there is no contradiction. Purists may argue that Tai Chi Chuan must have a martial content and taken literally the proper translation of the name Tai Chi Chuan is "supreme ultimate fist".

However, when all the principles of movement are applied all at once, then and only then can one be said to be truly doing Tai Chi; its martial context has no bearing on this definition. Without the principles it is simply not Tai Chi and without the martial aspects it is not Tai Chi Chuan. So this development could be reasonably thought of as 'Tai Chi without Chuan'. Personally I love the art of Tai Chi Chuan and enjoy the martial aspects as well as appreciate the health benefits. But I don't see any reason to alienate anyone for not training the way I do.

Introduction

This book is about you and the beginning of a journey of self-discovery, which will enable you to develop good health and understand your own body and its needs. A healthy mind needs a healthy body and with today's lifestyle becoming increasingly sedentary, we need to be aware of our physical, mental and health requirements.

By drawing on the wisdom from Traditional Chinese Medicine and the art of Tai Chi, you have all you need to begin a sensible programme of exercise, which can bring about a positive impact on your health, without having to invest heavily in time and spend a lot of money.

Each exercise is clearly explained within the context of your daily routine. Methodically going through the pages of this book will help you to understand what you are learning and practising. The full range of exercises and Tai Chi form here take little time to complete, so it can easily be accommodated into your busy daily life.

Allow yourself the luxury of a few moments of peace in a demanding world that seems to be moving too fast. Taking time out for yourself will be the first step on the road to improving your health. Simply by sitting down quietly and leaving your work to one side you will begin to improve your state of mind and therefore your mental health. There is only so much that you can take out of your health bank but an investment into your health, using the Yongquan Tai Chi, will pay you back in years to come – with interest.

The objective of this book is twofold; firstly to offer the novice a simple exercise programme for the enhancement of general well-being, especially for those whose lifestyles offers little opportunity to indulge in other forms of healthy activity. Secondly it serves as a stepping-stone to Tai Chi Chuan.

This book works as an easy to follow handbook by setting out the exercises in a clear and precise manner, serving as a visual reminder and theoretical reference.

You will find within this book some repetitions of phrases in slightly different ways. In my experience as a student (and teacher) I was reminded how to do something many times before it became part of my training. The purpose here is to offer those kinds of prompts in various ways to jog your own memory so that you too can learn.

There follows a set of Pa Tuan Chin, Chi Kung, and preparation exercises for beginners plus the Yongquan form itself, all of which have a significant good effect on your health. One very useful aspect of the Yongquan form is that it uses a small number of movements, so it can be practised anywhere and only takes a little time out of a busy day. Spending 20 minutes of practice a day is a great way to improve your health and enjoy life. At the end of the book are some helpful tips on how to treat common ailments.

Gentle exercise is not something that results in a great deal of cardio vascular fitness or fitness in general. The fitness being referred to here is that of the action of cell respiration in order to break down lactic acid. Putting the body under physical stress makes it deal with this build-up quicker, as with other forms of exercise such as running. Within the gentler arts this rarely happens and therefore fitness is not increased. Yet you will have some fitness and your heart will become stronger in its action. So devotees of Tai Chi or yoga will not necessarily be fit enough to run any great distance but health and fitness are parallel paths which at some point branch off in separate directions.

A certain amount of fitness is required for a healthy body but excess fitness as is required for some sports, can lead to long-term injuries. This is not a healthy state to be in, though there is much that can be done to prevent injuries, such as taking the time to warm up correctly and improving or maintaining our flexibility.

It is also worth remembering that an over enthusiastic approach to any exercise can be damaging. So remember to take things easy and never rush your journey. In time, many actions you initially found difficult will become easy.

This pure and mild form of exercise gently and, at first, imperceptibly changes your bodies and our vitality, lifting the spirit and clearing your minds.

It is often said that your health is your most valuable commodity for if you don't have your health you have nothing and it is also always good to remember that 'prevention is better than cure,' and cheaper too.

Chapter One
The Pa Taun Chin

Health Promoting Exercises

"It takes only five minutes to complete the whole set of exercises, providing a welcome break from the stress of your day".

Now we venture into what is new territory for the majority of people. You are about to begin a set of exercises that directly improve your health. They are not difficult and they will just take a little time to become natural. As always, regular practice is the key.

Before we embark upon the introduction and explanation of the Pa Tuan Chin, I would like to give a brief indication of how you should breathe within these exercises and Tai Chi as a whole. Breathing is achieved by using the diaphragm to make the space in the thoracic cavity for us to breathe. Air is taken in through the nose allowing the air to be warmed, filtered and humidified, with the tongue touching on the hard palate just behind the front top teeth. The muscles of the lower abdomen are relaxed which pushes them out slightly, allowing the diaphragm to lower, as it does in very young children and animals. Sadly this does nothing for a flat stomach but it is healthier.

It is more common for people to breathe using the Intercostal muscles of the rib cage; by flexing these muscles, the rib cage is lifted making space in the thoracic cavity for air to fill our lungs.

However this only allows for a relatively small amount of our lung capacity to fill up leaving a substantial area as dead space. Breathing in this way is often rapid and shallow being more than 12 times a minute at rest. Yet when the diaphragm is used to make the space for the air in our lungs, breathing is often slower and deeper as more oxygen enters our system.

The 'Pa Tuan Chin', also known as the Ba Duan Jin, is often translated as the Eight Silk Brocade. These are a set of breathing exercises that aid the body's natural health and healing. They are gentle movements which work by clearing meridians and strengthening organs, using our breathing co-ordinated with a stretch and relax action. They are very subtle in their action and it is only with regular practice that the benefits, such as prevention of illness are noticeable. Often we fail to see any difference until we begin to notice that others are affected by illness, which passes us by or affects us to a lesser extent. The Pa Tuan Chin takes little time out of an ordinary day to perform, taking only five minutes to complete. Unlike the Tai Chi form, it is not necessary to perform these exercises slowly; a steady rhythm which allows you to keep full control without hyperventilating or losing balance is sufficient.

There are a variety of different sets of Pa Tuan Chin which you can learn and practice. All of them offer similar health benefits in differing ways and some sets are more advanced. Those shown here offer the novice a simple first step to improving their health.

Practise first thing in the morning before you eat breakfast, though you may have a drink before. It can be done at any time during the day or even repeated in the same day as often as you wish, providing no food has been eaten within the hour beforehand. Visualisation (use of a mental imagery) is a technique which may be of some benefit with these exercises, for those who can use such techniques well.

As with the preparation exercises (and the Tai Chi form)

breathe in and out through the nose, unless physical obstruction prevents it. In the same way as with any form of physical exercise, should you feel any pain beyond a stretching sensation, stop doing the exercise and consult your doctor.

The Pa Tuan Chin does not have any particular order although it can flow from yang to yin. Nevertheless the first exercise 'Reaching to Heaven' is always the first performed and 'Vibrating the Back' is always last. The order presented here is one that follows a simple pathway of stretching the body and moving from high and low positions so as to not cause undue strain on the limbs, especially when beginning.

Remember to always breathe in and out of the nose unless otherwise instructed or a blockage prevents it. The rule is to breathe out on exertion and in on relaxation.

Each of these exercises are repeated eight times on both sides or alternately (four each side) as directed in the text. There is no need to extend your breath or stretch. Just breathe in and out and stretch for as long as you breathe out normally. Any deeper stretching can be done separately.

Exercise One – Reaching to Heaven

Awakens all the meridians and strengthens the internal organs

1

Stand with your legs shoulder width apart, breathe in and raise your hands to your head (your hands can touch your head but not each other).

2

Breathe out pressing your palms up and stretch, looking forward as you do so. In order to keep your balance, focus in front of you.

3

Ensure you keep your stability by focusing on something in front of you. Repeat eight times.

TIPS

Until you have attuned your sense of balance, you may find you have a problem in keeping the position even for the short amount of time it takes to breathe out. Don't worry, this will come with practice.

Fortifies the kidneys and the waist

1

Keep standing with your legs a shoulder width apart. Then simply breathe in.

2

Breathe out as you bend to touch your toes, only going as far as you can. Do not over-stretch if you cannot touch your toes.

3

Allow your legs to incline backwards and your head to just loll so that you end up looking backwards between your legs.

4

Do not hold your breath or prolong your expiration. Just breathe in and out whilst raising and lowering the upper body. Repeat eight times.

Exercise Three – Archer Draws Bow

Regulates the lungs and the upper jiao

1

Standing with your feet about one and a half shoulder widths apart, breathe in and raise your arms to chest height, as though 'hugging a barrel'.

2

Breathe out as you stretch into an archer position to either your right or left with one elbow pointing in the opposite direction to your outstretched hand.

3

Once you have finished breathing out, breathe in and return to your starting position with your hands in front of your chest.

4

Repeat this eight times on each side (one side then the other). Remember to stretch and not tense.

Soothes the spleen, stomach, liver and gall bladder

Standing in a shoulder width stance, breathe in and raise your arms to chest height, as though 'hugging a barrel'.

Then breathe out as you press one palm up and the other palm down; the top hand has its fingers pointing across the body with the bottom hand fingers pointing forwards.

Breathe in as you return to the start position.

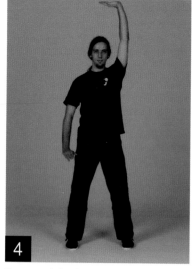

Repeat eight times on one side then eight times on the other.

Exercise Five – Spiral the Spine

Calms the mind and nerves, encourages healing of lesions, prevents exhaustion

1

Stand with your legs at shoulder width.

2

Breathe in then breathe out and turn as far round to your left or right. Look down with your eyes, trying not to tilt your spine in doing so.

3

Breathe back in as you return to face forward, pause for a second and then do the same again but turn in the opposite direction.

"Notice that the spine is not tilted".

Repeat eight times, alternating the direction.

Exercise Six – Stretch and Glare to the Horizon

Raises the Spirit

Once again standing with your feet one and a half shoulder widths apart, breathe in and raise your arms to chest height, as though 'hugging a barrel'.

Breathe out as you stretch one hand out in front of you and glare into the distance with your eyes (not too intensely).

Then breathe in as your hands meet in the middle.

Breathe out again as you stretch the other arm out in the same way. This is another alternating exercise so repeat eight times, four each side.

Exercise Seven – Shake Buttocks to Roll the Neck

Clears heat from the heart, calms the mind and removes hypertension

Whilst keeping in the wide stance of the previous exercise, rest your hands on your thighs and relax as much as possible.

Breathe in and then close your eyes as you lean over slightly from your waist, squarely to one side.

Breathe out as you use your hips to roll your neck; this is done by lifting your hips up on the same side as you have leant over to and then quickly sweeping it away giving a slight whipping action. Remember that the head is very heavy and this should not be done too vigorously. Once you have finished breathing out, breathe in as you return to your starting position and start again. This is not an easy one to learn. The key parts are to relax your neck muscles, keep your back flat even though you lean to one side and do not try to roll your neck too hard.

Exercise Eight – Vibrate the Back

Calms the whole system, resettles the organs and meridians

1

Standing with your legs shoulder width apart, make loose fists with your hands and place them in the small of your back to support your kidneys.

2

Breathe in, then roll up onto the balls off your feet making a slight arch with your body looking up at 45° and gently bounce as you breathe out through your nose, breathing in as you face forward standing flat on your feet.

> "Focus your eyes on a point above you to help keep your balance. Remember to breathe out through your nose".

3

It is very important to breathe out through your nose as your neck muscles will help to control your breath. Repeat eight times.

Chapter Two
The Chi Kung

"These standing positions can cause the heart beat to rise to 140 Bpm".

The Chi Kung always seems to have had an air of mystery surrounding it. If mentioned it usually has, or gives the feeling of something a little bit 'out there, hippy-ish or spacey'.On the contrary, the Chi Kung is an ancient practice that has been refined over many years and is rooted in practicalities. In point of fact it is quite a good way of grounding you rather than sending you away with the fairies, if it is taught, encouraged and practised correctly.

Chi Kung has a long history; quite when its origins began is a discussion for the academics. Over many years there have been innovations, developments and refinements that have led to many different styles and methods of achieving similar aims. No single method is necessarily more correct than any other. These differences may well reflect the variations in the desired outcome of Chi Kung training. Therefore, an open mind should be adopted when viewing those forms of Chi Kung unknown to you or different from yours.

Over the years the knowledge and wisdom that have been attained by our predecessors have gone into what we teach and practice. We should gain comfort from the fact that we stand on the shoulders of those who have gone before us. We begin not knowing what we are doing but through the patient direction of our teachers we learn and grow.

First let me explain a little of the terminology. It is important to know the meanings of the words you are using but not to worry too much about the semantics; it is the act that is important not its name. There are a number of words used to describe this practice and Chi Kung is one of them. The word Chi means air and/or energy and the word Kung (Kung is sometimes written Gong or Gung) means work. So the Chi Kung means you are doing air or energy work. Many people call standing, breathing postures Chi Kung but there are differences in how such exercises are done. Those exercises which improve health and general well-being are accurately called Chi Kung. The Pa Tuan Chin can also be described as Chi Kung, however as it has a name of its own it is more commonly referred to as such.

Another term you may hear for such practice is the Nei Kung. This means internal work and although the postures may look similar there is a lot more to this. This practice is mainly the domain of the martial artists, specifically those of the internal schools (Nei Chia as opposed to the Wai Chia) and has the purpose of building up Internal energy or Chi / Qi for use in combat but has the added benefit of increasing health and vitality.

> "Empty yourself of everything.
> Let the mind become still"
> – Tao Te Ching.

The postures shown on the following pages are Chi Kung, that is to say that they are specifically shown in a manner for the benefit of health and not for martial use. These postures follow a simple pattern of building, gathering and storing energy, mild yet effective. For proper Nei Kung training you need the attention of an experienced and well versed Sifu.

How to Stand

To begin with you may find the postures a little difficult to do; it is amazing how standing still can be so much like hard work. Each posture should be held for about five minutes each. Begin by holding the first posture for 3–5 minutes. Once this is achieved add the following exercise and continue as before until you can do all three postures one after another for the full 15 minutes.

Should you have a physical disadvantage that prevents you from standing in these postures for this length of time, you can use a high stool to rest against whilst maintaining the hands position. If you use this method then remember not to sit fully on the stool but to rest one half, not one buttock, of your bottom on the forward edge. I have added one last additional aspect to this Chi Kung for your benefit, which you may find helps to keep your mind quiet for the time that you practise. Use your mind to visualise a white light, picture it flowing down from the heavens; allow it to fill you, the room, your house, flat or area that you stand in.

> "The Tao nourishes those who have the wisdom to stand like a tree – mightiest of trees began as a tiny seed and the driest of rivers can be flooded by the smallest raindrops – through constant practice, a little everyday, you will grow".

First Posture – Building Energy

Keep your back straight. Initially this is going to be a little difficult to do as we all have a tendency to lean back, but by using a mirror to one side of you it is possible to check your posture and correct any leaning, whether it is forwards or backwards.

Second Posture – Gathering Energy

Keep your back straight as with the entire set of Chi Kung postures. This posture can be used as a resting position from the first posture before returning back to building energy, helping to lengthen your training.

Continue to keep your back straight. Your heartbeat can rise to 140 Bpm just standing like this – a surprising workout for the heart.

With patient, routine practice you will find that you begin to feel your energy to be more bountiful. Follow the guidelines and enjoy your practice. Never rush – just clear your mind and breathe in and out in a relaxed manner. Keep your tongue gently pressed on the hard palate behind your top front teeth and open or close your eyes as you wish. Try to focus exactly on what you are doing (standing still and breathing) by forgetting everything that you have to do or have been doing.

The analogy of the dripping tap filling the bucket is very apt here. There is little to be gained by doing one-off heavy sessions every few days or every week. You will find it easier and far more beneficial to do just a little bit everyday.

By practising the Chi Kung you reintroduce yourself to the spiritual and energetic state that you were in when you were a baby.

If you watch a child of 0 months – 3 years breathing as they move, rest or sleep, you should be able to see that they breathe using their diaphragm; their chest doesn't rise and fall as much but their abdomen goes in and out. Also babies can look/stare at everything all at once and find it difficult to focus on one thing, yet are able to look at the world all day without blinking. There is a reference to this in the Tao Te Ching.

Also, with virtually no muscle power they can hold onto something, often hair or something of value that you desperately want back, so tightly that it is a struggle for an adult to retrieve it. This is an example of babies using their natural energy without thought or effort. You have this power too but you have simply forgotten it.

Some people naturally have more available energy than others but this does not prevent you from building your energy up to be strong too. Some people get quick results while others take longer. This does not matter – what matters is that you practise. This energy is all around us all the time. You are merely learning to access it at your own will and for your own enhancement.

It is not a thought or a mental projection but a sense, a vibe or a feeling that you experience, not as tangible as a handshake but not so elusive as to evade your senses. It is an experience shaped by your own perspective and although you may find it difficult to put into words, the experience is real.

Chapter Three
Preparation

"Suitable for all ages".

So we begin. These exercises are designed to stretch and relax all the major muscle groups and tendons as well as to warm up the joints prior to the practice of Tai Chi. Working from the ankles upwards these exercises move fluidly from one to the next. This encourages blood circulation, giving nourishment to the muscles and warmth to the joints in order to help prevent cramp and strain injuries. The movements are easy to learn and remember. Though requiring little in the way of skill, they must be done correctly so as to avoid injuring oneself.

These exercises are suitable for people of any age and are of great value to those who are unused to doing much, if any physical exercise. They are also perfect for the busy executive at work as they require little space and will act as an aid to relaxation. Physical relaxation also contains a psychological aspect. This takes time to cultivate and cannot be achieved without slowing down the thought processes. It is an essential attitude for everyone,

whether or not they practise Tai Chi, as the stresses of modern day living have many detrimental effects on the human body leading to many health problems. Another bonus to the attainment of relaxation is that the meridians (energy pathways within the body) allow the body's natural Qi flow more easily.

Warm ups are, in general, an important part of all kinds of physical exercise. They are something we often ignore or avoid yet they exist for a good reason. Before starting any physical workout, whether it be hard or the more gentle, it is important to prepare the body for the exercise it is about to embark on. Proper warming up leads to fewer injuries, by helping to strenghten and/or stretch your muscles, joints and tendons. This in turn prepares your body for the increased level of exercise you are about to undertake.

Age often plays a large part in whether or not we take such preparation seriously; when we are young our bodies are more flexible and robust, usually healing quickly. For the young, warming up seems more like a drudgery than a necessity but as we age our bodies become less flexible and stiffer so the need to warm up is greater. Nonetheless it is still wise for everyone of any age to warm up correctly when preparing to exercise. It is useful to get into a routine of performing these warm ups just prior to practising the form so it becomes a regular part of your everyday training and not something you have to work hard at remembering to do.

The exercises shown here start by working on the ankles and then move up the body, exercising each set of joints and muscle groups as you progress. Be sure to have plenty of room around you before you start to allow yourself freedom of movement. Remember don't over do it to begin with – start slowly, doing only what you can and gently work towards deeper stretching. This way you will not hurt yourself and eventually you will be able to accomplish the movements to their full range. Breathe in and out through the nose on all these exercises unless you have a specific problem in doing so.

Exercise One – Knee Circling

Stretches the muscles and tendons of the lower limbs from the knees down

1

The first warm up is a knee circling action. Placing the hands on the top of the knees but putting no weight on them, look forward at eye level.

2

Now keeping your feet flat on the floor begin to circle the knees to the right or left for an even number of times.

3

Then repeat this action in the opposite direction for an equal number of times

WHAT DOES THIS DO?

This primarily warms up the ankle ligaments, tendons and muscles of the lower leg plus it has a warming effect on the muscles of the thighs and the ligaments and tendons of the knees. Remember not to put any weight on your hands and to circle your knees at an even, steady pace.

Exercise Two – Squatting

Keeps the tendons warm and helps stretch them further

Put your feet together.

Slowly lower yourself down keeping your feet flat on the floor.

Ideally, you should sit or squat on your heels but if you can't manage this, go as low as possible keeping your feet flat on the floor.

TIPS

This picture shows the ideal position but don't worry if you can't lower down this far. Just go as low as you can, keeping your feet flat on the floor. Slowly over a period of time you will get down to a squatting position. Remember not to hold your breath whilst doing this or any other exercise.

Exercise Three – Lifting the Knee

Warms the hip joints and gently stretches the buttock muscles

1

Stand on your right leg, raising the left leg holding below the knee with both hands. Pull the knee up towards the chest.

2

The standing leg should be kept slightly bent but your back should be kept straight.

3

Stretch both legs a number of times and at the very least twice.

"This is an excellent exercise to help improve your balance as well as gently strengthening your legs".

Exercise Four – Bow Stretch

Stretches the groin area

1

Place your feet a shoulder width and a half to two shoulder widths apart with your feet parallel.

2

Bend one knee (slightly pushed out) and keep the other straight. Then slightly incline your upper body and turn your hips towards the straight leg.

3

Do it on both sides, keeping both feet flat on the floor.

REMEMBER

The bow stretch, like any other, should only be pushed as far as you can go to the edges of comfort – never bounce.

Exercise Five – Turn to look up

Warms the spine, stretching in an upward, twisting motion

1

With feet shoulder width apart, make loose fists and place them together with the backs of the palms in the small of your back, resting against the lower edges of the kidneys.

2

Facing forward breathe in through your nose then breathe out as you turn to look round and up as far as you can.

3

Upon reaching your limit, breathe in turning back round to face forward.

4

Pause for a second then do the same in the opposite direction. Repeat for eight turns.

Excellent for relaxing tense muscles in the shoulders and calming the mind

Again standing with your feet a shoulder width apart, breathe in slowly through the nose as you lift your arms straight up in front of you.

Continue to lift the arms until they are above your head, palms facing down.

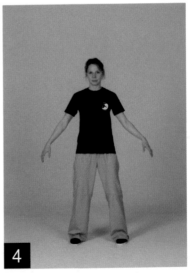

Breathe out through your nose as you lower your arms on an outward circle until you reach the bottom.

Repeat for a number of times or usually for a few minutes. Remember to do this slowly.

1

Stand with your feet just over a shoulder width apart. With fingers in the position shown above, raise your right arm up in front of you, breathing in, gently leaning back.

2

Breathe out as the left hand reaches down towards your right foot. Breathe in as you rise allowing the right hand to swing up out in front, the left being closer to your head.

3

Then allow the right hand to reach down to your left foot in the same way as before, breathing out as you go down and in as you come up.

4

The aim is to eventually be able to touch the floor whilst the other hand is pointed upwards. Repeat a number of times.

Following these preparation exercises will enable your body to prepare itself for performing the Tai Chi form and therefore should be done just prior to it. Through correct warming up the body is able to function properly in the chosen activity. It is important to remember to take the time to warm up to minimise the risk of strain or injury. As warm-ups are not a competition, you should only stretch as far as you can easily reach. With time you will be able to do more. Neither the warm ups or the form take very long to do – they are easy to fit into anyone's busy day. In doing so it allows time for oneself. Regular practice will help combat stress and improve your general health.

Remember that the effects of such training are cumulative, which is why you should try to incorporate these exercises into a regime that you can include as part of your lifestyle. Of course before you do so you have to become familiar with the exercises and this is best achieved through repetition. Gradually the body acquires the necessary coordination in order to perform the movements correctly. Soon you will be doing the exercises with little thought. The same is true of the form which is dealt with later in the book.

Sudden spasms of hard training dispersed by periods of little or no activity yields little in the way of attainment within our field of endeavour, so remember to begin by adding five minutes of exercise to your daily workload and slowly increase this as time passes.

It is not my intention to tell you exactly how much you should do but if you can eventually work up to 20 minutes a day of warm ups, Form, Pa Tuan Chin and Chi Kung you will be doing well, and in a very short time you will begin to notice some changes in your health and vitality. This is only the start of a cascade of new developments you will experience. Keep it going and let it grow and soon you could find yourself practising for an hour or more without noticing.

One last thought, the mighty Oak starts from an acorn so begin small and work up; it is not a race, good luck.

Chapter Four
The Yongquan Form
(Bubbling Spring)

"Perfect these 30 moves to improve circulation, alert the mind, increase energy and reduce stress".

This is a vital part of your aspirations to become and stay healthy. Keeping in mind the Chinese saying 'a moving hinge never goes rusty' in order that we keep robust and strong we should keep flexible in mind and body. We all move around throughout our days to one extent or another but that is not enough to nourish the body or calm the mind. This is achieved through arts like yoga and Tai Chi; the gentle arts have far more to offer than can be perceived just by looking and observing. Here we are using a simple form of Tai Chi designed specifically for health. The regular practice of this form holds many benefits; improved circulation, a greater alertness of mind, increased energy and, stress reduction.

To begin with let me tell you a little about the history of Tai Chi and the Yongquan form which you are about to learn. The art of Tai Chi Chuan has a recordable history of around 500 years, though its origins undoubtedly pre-date its earliest writings. Its health benefits are a direct result of old Taoist wisdom,

following nature's rules. These principles apply to all the different styles of Tai Chi Chuan; each form follows the particular style of a family or group. There are five major family styles; namely the Chen, Yang, Wu, Sun and little Woo (now commonly referred to as Hao style). Like branches of a tree they all share a common root and can be traced back to the Chen Family of Chen Chiagou village.

In the early 1960s to mid 1970s most of the Tai Chi schools began developing short forms. These made the study of Tai Chi a little easier and were often better balanced, as most long forms are both repetitive and biased to one side or the other (usually the right). These short forms take less time to learn. They mostly involve equal left and right side movement whilst keeping all the necessary elements to maintain the beneficial martial and health qualities.

In the West the appeal for its health benefits brought about a new development, the innovation of health oriented forms for those not wishing to study the martial aspects.

Our branch of Tai Chi Chuan finds its roots in the Old Yang style long form, which was the first variation that was ever implemented in the Tai Chi Chuan world. It was created by Yang Lu Chan (1799–1872) who was renowned as a great master of Tai Chi Chuan and even today is still revered as one of, if not the greatest, master that ever lived. Since then there have been many modifications made to the various styles of Tai Chi Chuan. So long as they adhere to the principles of the art and have a lineage back to its recordable origins they have the right to be called Tai Chi Chuan.

I innovated the Yongquan health form by taking aspects of the Kwon Ping Yang long form and joining them together into a much shorter form. This is intended to give everyone an easy to learn Tai Chi form, which due to its small number of movements can be practised almost anywhere and can be incorporated into anyone's daily routine virtually regardless of lifestyle. The structure of the form flows from right to left in a wave like motion, using not only both right and left sides but also the whole body in one co-ordinated flowing motion. Beginning and ending in the same place, it gives you all the health benefits of Tai Chi while greatly reducing training time as the majority of the martial aspects have been removed. So in a sense you are practising 'Tai Chi without Chuan'.

Tai Chi has some well-defined levels of attainment. Briefly for this style they are as follows:

- **Beginner**
Learning form and associated exercises
- **Elementary**
Begin learning the first four of twelve internal principles
- **Intermediate**
Begin learning the next four of the twelve principles
- **Advanced**
Begin learning the last four principles
- **Sifu**
Able to do all the principles and has full knowledge of Tai Chi Chuan as a whole art, given papers of introduction from their Sifu and nowadays also a certificate.

In Tai Chi you should never have your weight evenly balanced, except momentarily at commencement and completion. Your weight therefore is constantly moving backwards and forwards. This is very good for strengthening the legs as well as helping to pump blood around and back up to the heart from the lower extremities which will help to prevent varicose veins. For the beginner this is hard on the legs at first as we are not used to keeping our legs bent while standing and even less so when we move. However, it does not take long for the body to adjust and in a short time you will find that your legs are stronger and more mobile.

The movements of the form are naturally circular in character, much like the form itself; beginning and ending in the same place it started. From a purely biomechanical point of view the gentle, steady motion and regular tensing and relaxing, tones the muscle. Combine this with the postural considerations and it makes for a healthy workout that maintains health and good posture. Within time the body will move as a unit, which makes the actions of the body more powerful. Mastery of this form does not take the long years of hard study that it does with Tai Chi Chuan (the fighting art) so that the full range of health benefits of Tai Chi Chuan can be accessed quicker and easier.

To realise the full potential for health in this art will require the student to practise to a level equal to that of the Elementary level going onto Intermediate level. For this you will need to be able to move as a single unit and therefore achieve Sung Chin which can be translated as relaxed force. Once this has been achieved there is little need for the health student to take their training any further unless of course they wish to do so. By this stage regular practice will be something of a good habit, which will allow you to continue gaining and maintaining your good health.

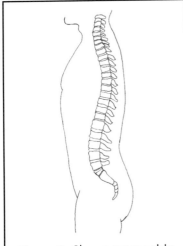

Figure 1. Shows reasonable posture but here the chest and the coccyx are slightly stuck out.

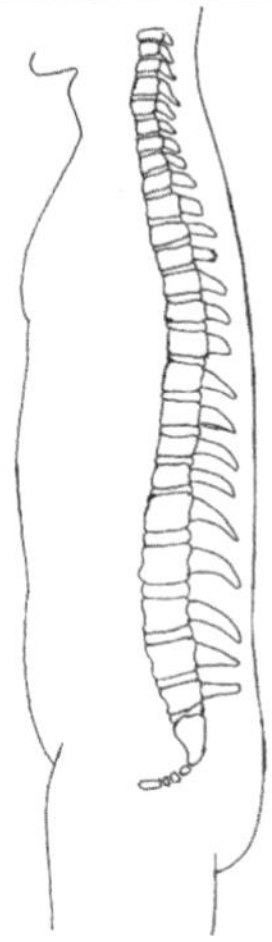

Figure 2. Here we see proper posture as it should be in Tai Chi. Neither the chest nor the coccyx are stuck out and the lower back has a flatter appearance.

First of all always start the form facing the same direction. By this I mean that if you practise in a room or outside, begin facing the same wall or view. This way you will have a visual reminder of where you should be facing at various points throughout the form. When you are about to begin the form, stand with your legs a shoulder width apart with your feet pigeon toed and your legs unlocked.

Take a full breath, as deep as you can, and then let it out through your mouth in one quick blast. This will help your body to be in roughly the correct position by hollowing the chest and lifting the back. Always start facing in the same direction, for your visual reminders.

Allow your shoulders to be rounded – square shoulders are good for the army but maintain a level of tension that we do not need in Tai Chi.

Bind the coccyx which means tucking it in by rolling forward the pubic bone in a slightly upward curve. Ensure that you are not simply thrusting your pelvis forward which does not have the effect of straightening the spine that binding the coccyx does.

To start with, here are the names of each of the movements in the Yongquan form. You will see that there are only 30 moves to perfect, which start and finish in the same place. Allow your body to move, just breathe as you would do normally and let nature do the rest.

The names of the Yongquan (bubbling spring) form:

1) Commencement
2) Ward off (right)
3) Hold ball
4) Ward off (left)
5) Grasp birds tail
6) Press
7) Roll back
8) Push
9) Hold ball
10) Ward off (right)
11) Grasp bird's tail (right)
12) Press
13) Roll back
14) Push
15) Single whip
16) Turn – raise hands (right)
17) Hands strum the lute
18) Turn (left) – hold ball
19) White crane cools its wings
20) Turn to position Lotus
21) Lotus kick
22) Shoot Tiger with bow
23) Retreat, double parry
24) Kick and deflect (right)
25) Step up punch
26) Clear hands
27) Push
28) Cross arms
29) Carry Tiger home to mountain
30) Conclusion.

Form 1 – Commencement

COMMENCEMENT: Stand straight (as if you are facing North).

Draw arms to shoulder height.

Draw your arms back towards your shoulders and then push the palms down.

Lower arms to just below your waist, bending your knees as your hands pass your waist (lightly pushing your knees outwards). From here on do not straighten your knees until completion of the form.

Form 2 – Ward off (right)

5

Turn 45° to your right, moving 60% of your weight forwards (facing north east). Bring your right arm up to your chest height, as if cradling a balloon against you. Allow your left hand to remain, palm facing down by your left hip, WARD OFF RIGHT.

"In motion the whole body should be light and agile, when one part moves all parts move as though threaded together".

Form 3 – Hold Ball

6

Step in putting all your weight onto your right leg. Bring your left palm in until the palms face each other. HOLD BALL.

7

Step round to the opposite 45° with your left leg (north west).

Form 4 – Ward off (left)

8

Draw the left arm under the right, bringing the weight forwards on to the left leg as the hands pass.

9

WARD OFF LEFT, cradling a balloon in your left arm, allowing your right hand to stay by your right hip with 60% of your weight forwards (north west).

"The postures should be without defects, hollows or projections from the proper posture; in motion the Form should not become disjointed".

Form 5 – Grasp Bird's Tail

10

Raise the right hand palm up, letting the fingers touch the left hand, folding the palms opposite. This is the beginning of GRASP BIRD'S TAIL.

11

Roll back 70% of your weight, drawing your hands to the level of, and just in front of your right hip, continuing GRASP BIRD'S TAIL.

"Your feet should be rooted like a mountain, your hands like clouds".

Form 6 – Press

12

Roll 60% of your weight forwards bringing your hands together in the PRESS form (in front of your solar plexus parallel to your forward foot).

13

Open your hands (as if to catch a beach ball).

"The spine should be a plumb line from the coccyx to the crown of the head".

Form 7 – Roll Back

14

ROLL BACK 90% of your weight, lifting the left toes, rounding the hands down.

Form 8 – Push

15

Roll 60% of your weight forwards, raising your hands to chest height in the PUSH form.

"Sink your mind (Chi) to the centre (Tan-Tien) found 2 inches below the navel to calm the thoughts process".

Form 9 – Hold Ball

16

Step in with your right foot and HOLD BALL with your weight fully on your left foot.

18

WARD OFF RIGHT, 60% of your weight forward (north east).

Form 10 – Ward off (right)

17

Step round to the opposite 45°, this time with your right foot (north east). Draw the right arm under the left, again bringing the weight forward as the hands pass. Bring your right arm up to your chest height, as if cradling a balloon against you, allowing your left hand to remain, palm facing down by your left hip, in to WARD OFF RIGHT form.

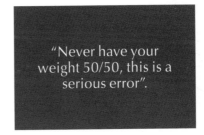

"Never have your weight 50/50, this is a serious error".

Form 11 – Grasp Bird's Tail (right)

19

Raise the left hand with palm facing up. Let the fingers touch the right hand folding the palms so that they touch. This is the beginning of GRASP BIRD'S TAIL.

20

Continue GRASP BIRD'S TAIL by rolling back 70% of your weight as you draw both your hands to the level of, and just in front of, your left hip.

"The weight moves constantly back and forth like waves on the sea shore".

Form 12 – Press

21

Roll 60% of your weight forwards, bringing your hands together in the PRESS form (in front of your solar plexus parallel to your forward foot).

22

Open your hands (as if to catch a beach ball).

"Your hands should be relaxed but not limp, lightly extend your fingers".

Form 13 – Roll Back Form

23

ROLL BACK 90% of your weight, lifting the right toes, rounding the hands down.

Form 14 – Push

24

Then roll 60% of your weight forwards, raising your hands to chest height in the PUSH form.

25

"Each movement should cascade one on to another like water flowing".

Roll your weight slightly further forwards to 80% on the right-side, turning both palms out, with your left hand close to the right-side of the chest (droop your left elbow). Turn your left foot to face west.

26

Sweep hands and body to the west and roll 60% of your weight forwards on the left foot, as you reach the end of this movement turn up your left foot and form a beak with your right hand. To form a beak firstly put your index and little finger tips together. Then place your two middle fingers directly behind them and your thumb at the front to push them together.

"Never rush, take your time, enjoy each moment and be in each moment".

27

Roll 70% of your weight back to your right side, bringing the right hand with you. Let your left hand roll out in a big arc, anti clockwise.

28

Ending at your right cheek, as your left foot steps in beside your right foot. 100% of your weight should be on your right foot.

Turn your left foot round in an arc shape to the south west. Roll your foot down from the heel, ending in a push with your left hand at solar plexus height.

SINGLE WHIP.

Turn, pivoting on your left heel, bringing your left hand to touch the side of the beak.

Drop the beak, moving right hand down to waist height, allowing the left hand to follow a little.

Form 16 – Turn Hands (right)

33

Draw up the right hand as an open hand, as if pulling up a zip on a coat. Finish with your left hand under your right elbow and both hands out in front of your chest as RAISE HANDS RIGHT (facing north east).

Form 17 – Hands strum the Lute

34

Keep 90% of your weight on your left and step with your right leg facing eastwards and only your heel on the floor (toes raised) – HANDS STRUM THE LUTE.

35

Turn on your right heel, anti clockwise. When you can turn no further put your weight onto your right foot. Drop your right hand as you do so as if scooping up a huge snowball, with your right hand underneath.

36

With palms facing each other, HOLD BALL, weight on your right foot.

37

"Shift your weight smoothly".

Squash the ball as you roll back your weight by drawing your hips back. Look at a point on the floor about three metres in front of you.

Form 19 – White Crane Cools its Wings

38

39

Separate your hands as you straighten up. Bring your right hand up to head height with palm facing out slightly. Simultaneously bring your left hand to your left hip with palm facing down. WHITE CRANE COOLS ITS WINGS, facing west.

Catch on your left side by raising your left hand to shoulder height on your left side. Bring your right hand over the top to your left shoulder and look left. Note the position of the hands in the following picture. This is the correct position for the hands.

"All movement in Tai Chi originates from the centre (Tan-Tien)".

Form 20 – Turn to Position Lotus

40

41

TURN TO POSITION LOTUS: turn clockwise on your left heel as far as you can, then put your weight on your left foot. Continue the turn on your right heel until your right foot is pointing south (or as close as possible). All the while maintain your arms at around shoulder height.

Transition picture.

"Complete each action and allow the motion to trickle over to the next without a pause but do not clip the movements".

42

Step with your left foot round just in front of your right foot landing only on your heel (do not put your weight on this foot yet). Contine your turn until you can't turn the foot any further, allowing your weight to rest on the left foot then. Now you face west again but with your right foot in front, and 90% of your weight on your left foot.

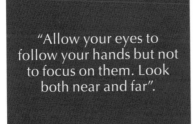

"Allow your eyes to follow your hands but not to focus on them. Look both near and far".

43

Transition picture.

44

Catch on your right side by dropping your right hand and raising it out-stretched on your right side. At the same time raise your left hand over the top to your right shoulder.

Form 21 – Lotus Kick

45

46

LOTUS KICK: circle your right leg round clockwise as you face west, bringing in both your hands, palms facing towards your foot coming from the opposite direction. Slap your foot. Put your foot down slightly wider and further forward from where it came.

Drop your hands together to around waist height then separate your hands with the left leading forward, the right drawing behind the right ear.

"For some people this manoeuvre proves difficult at first. Negate this by performing the same motion but only bring your knee up and slap that".

Form 22 – Shoot Tiger with Bow

47

SHOOT TIGER WITH BOW: left hand raised as a punch at shoulder height straight forward whilst your right hand is drawn back at head height just behind your right ear. 60% of your weight should be forward, facing west.

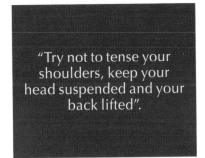

"Try not to tense your shoulders, keep your head suspended and your back lifted".

Form 23 – Retreat, Double Parry

48

RETREAT, DOUBLE PARRY: roll 70% of your weight back on to your left leg bringing your left hand to the right side of your face and your right hand to the left side of your groin.

49

Step in with your right foot as you put your left palm to your right mid-forearm. Make a loose fist with your right hand.

Form 24 – Kick and Deflect (right)

50

KICK AND DEFLECT RIGHT: circle both right hand and foot towards the north west, stepping forwards in the same direction.

51

Open the arms wide as you move 60% of your weight forward.

"Don't speed up the connecting movements keep to one constant speed all the way through".

52

Step with your left hand and foot forwards in a slight semi circle, cutting the width between your feet by half. Move 60% of your weight forward onto your left foot.

Form 25 – Step up punch

53

Punch with your right hand at groin height with your left palm hovering an inch above your right mid-forearm. STEP UP PUNCH.

Form 26 – Clear hands

54

Circle your left hand under your right elbow as you roll 70% of your weight back. Both palms are facing up at the end of roll back. CLEAR HANDS.

"Move as one unit and you will have attained sung chin".

Form 27 – Push

55

Turn your palms over and PUSH, facing west.

Form 28 – Cross Arms

56

CROSS ARMS: turn your hips to the north east and fold your arms with the right arm in front of the left. They should be separated by approximately 6 inches.

"Through roundness you achieve a flow".

57

Stretch up with both hands and step directly behind you (feet parallel).

Form 29 – Carry Tiger Home to Mountain

Separate your arms by bringing your right arm over to the right side of your body whilst bringing 80% of your weight with it. Swooping low as if to pick up a bundle from the floor, CARRY TIGER HOME TO MOUNTAIN.

Bring the weight back on to your left foot as you bring both hands up and step in with your right foot. Make sure both feet end up pigeon-toed in the way you began.

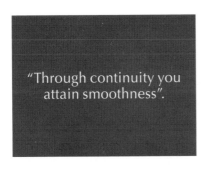

"Through continuity you attain smoothness".

Settle your hands down as you straighten (but not lock) your legs.

Form 30 – Conclusion

61

CONCLUSION.

62

Breath three times before you move away, allowing yourself to settle.

> "'Kung Fu' means work well done; to practise regularly is to practise kung fu. It leads to understanding and knowing oneself – its rewards are many, one is good health".

Chapter Five
Corrections and Errors

Inevitably there will be errors that creep into your training from time to time. Here I will tell you of some of these potential errors and ways to correct them. Never be disheartened; we learn only by making mistakes. It is sometimes thought that once you can do the form, you can do Tai Chi. However this is not the case, you then need to practise in order to improve your movements. This constant practice allows you to refine your posture and co-ordination, helping you to circulate your Chi and maintain your health.

To begin with, practise the form so that you reach the point where you can do it without having to think too much about what move comes next. Once this has been achieved you can begin to start correcting the movement and posture. Having just learnt the form means that you will have many variations in your form that are not in the original and need to be removed. This is quite normal and will be the case for some time until the form is refined enough the whole way through. Do not be discouraged by this – it is the way with everything that is

TIPS

Ensure that the feet, and therefore the body, are pointing/ facing in the right direction.

In each of the postures make sure the knee comes to the line of the toes but no further.

All forward steps land heel first and backward steps land toes first.

Roll the weight slowly onto the foot as your weight moves forward.

Make sure that the weighting is 60/40 – 70/30 – 80/20 – 90/10 – 100% depending on the requirements of the step.

Keep your legs bent and don't straighten them until you finish the form.

Never lock your legs – this is a lazy way to stand and is not good for your posture or joints.

a skill, there are always refinements to be made.

First of all it is important to get the footwork right, as the hands are so easy to mimic students often focus on them and forget about their feet.

These are just the first of many adjustments you will need to make to the form. Take it step by step. You have a lifetime to perfect it so don't try to rush things. Correct each one at your own pace and have another look at them if and when it is necessary. Slowly, your form will begin to look more and more correct. Patience is something that, if you don't have now, you will develop soon enough. It is something that will not be too difficult to cultivate as the practice of the form can be enjoyable due to its stress relieving qualities.

Now we can address the physical aspects of your posture that you need to incorporate into the form:

Suspending the head

Lifting the back

Rounding the shoulders and relaxing the elbows

Hollowing the chest

Centering the coccyx

These five postural considerations are necessary to improve your posture throughout the form but should not be limited to the form. Try incorporating them into your daily life. Correct posture will help solve a lot of problems, as any 'Alexander Technique' therapist will tell you.

Suspending the Head

As if being pulled up by a string, not unlike a marionette, allow the head to be lifted. The string pulling you up would be like a plumb line that travels down through the last third of your head where the cervical spine supports the skull. This lowers the chin and gives most people the feeling that they are falling forwards. This is not the case but is due to the way so many of us normally stand with our chins high and heads back slightly. The feeling of falling or leaning forwards is due to the repositioning of the fluid in the cochlea in the middle ear. This fires the nerve endings to send information to the brain telling you that you are leaning forwards. In a short space of time this will readjust itself.

You may notice that your eyes now have to be fully open in order for you to see up ahead of you instead of the half closed appearance you have with your chin high. Also with the head in the correct position, this allows optimal blood flow to the brain and helps to keep us more alert.

Lifting the Back

The spine has a natural curve in it although this is not always obvious. The muscle surrounding the spine and all the muscle and skin around the whole of our backs fills in a lot of the space of those curves. So when in its correct position the back can look flat even though it still retains its normal curvature.

We should never slouch or lean as this causes all sorts of problems e.g. slouching depresses our diaphragm so we can't breathe properly.

Lifting the back can be achieved in a similar fashion to suspending the head. But another way is to inhale as deep as you can and then release the air in one quick exhalation. This will automatically lift your back. Then you only have to keep it there, which takes practice. Although this will seem difficult at first, it is in fact better for you as, with the spine correctly aligned the bulk muscle will relax more. In turn this allows for greater blood circulation and therefore rids the muscles of their waste materials and replenishes their food requirements more easily.

Rounding of the Shoulders and Relaxing the Elbows

As we are growing up it is common to hear adults say 'straighten your back, don't slouch, stick out your chest, shoulders back'. But this is in fact not a natural posture. It can lead to headaches, backaches and all sorts of other complications.

Allowing our shoulders to relax is one of the easier aspects to take on board. They are meant to droop down but not forward as that would mean that you are not actually lifting your back. Again this facilitates good blood circulation; when the shoulders are relaxed along with the surrounding muscles, it will be beneficial to the upper limbs, neck and head and this is made much easier by the muscles having good tone.

When the shoulders and the trapezious muscles are relaxed it also helps prevent headaches and alleviate stress. The result is that the hands warm up and the head goes cool. The relaxing of the elbows should complement the relaxation of the shoulders and prevent any blockage in the flow of your natural energy. Throughout most of the form the shoulders are kept in a relaxed position and the elbows and wrists are held in their appropriate postures below the level of the shoulders. This is the most relaxed way to maintain the structure of the form and not introduce tension whilst keeping the form correct. The exceptions to this rule are postures like Single Whip where the wrist is held above the shoulder for the purposes of correct application and correctness of the form. There are a few positions in this little form where this exception applies, yet this is still in keeping with the principles of Tai Chi Chuan. Follow the pictures of the form and note the correct position of the hands.

Hollow the Chest

Hollowing or relaxing the chest helps to release tension that builds up in this area and helps to keep proper posture. It also facilitates proper breathing; by relaxing our chests we allow the torso to relax. This means that the diaphragm is under less tension through improper posture. The diaphragm should be the main muscle used to breathe although it's more often the case that, most people tend to breathe with their intercostal muscles. These make space for the air to enter our lungs by raising the chest but this is not the best way or the most natural way to breathe.

You may remember from school days, being shown a bell jar with two balloons connected to a 'Y' tube, a cellophane base and a rubber bung in the top. The teacher would pull down the cellophane base and the balloons would inflate with the explanation that this is how we breathe.

Yet especially at that time and probably even now (unless you have already been taught otherwise) we breathe raising our chests. The bell jar couldn't

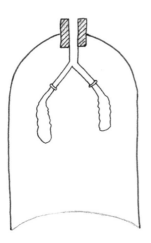

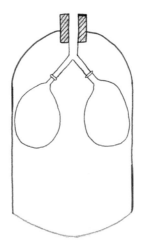

Fig 3. The bell jar above represents the chest. As our diapraghms are raised, our lungs deflate.

Fig 4. The bell jar above now shows how our lungs inflate as our diapraghms are lowered.

This is the correct method of breathing, showing how our lungs can inflate and deflate without the need to raise and lower our chests. If we need to fill our lungs to their full capacity we would employ the intercostal muscles as well.

do that. In fact it is healthier to breathe using the diaphragm; it means that we take more air into more of our lung space. This, in turn, tends to slow our breathing down as we are already getting enough oxygen from the extra amount of air we are now drawing into our lungs.

When we breathe the ribcage should not rise and fall as it often does. It is better for the lower abdomen to be relaxed and push out as we breathe in and pull in as we breathe out. Due to the abdominal breathing you tend to lose your flat stomach slightly as the muscles need to be relaxed in order to breathe correctly.

Diaphragmatic breathing also aids the circulation of blood and keeps all the internal organs in their correct positions. The movements of the form will then allow them to gently massage one another. It should be pointed out that abdominal breathing is not always advisable for example if you are a runner. This is because we use our abdominal muscles to help us to run faster so we need to breathe using our chest and intercostal muscles. So when you run or do any other kind of sport that requires a tense abdomen, breathe via your chest and at all other times use your diaphragm.

Centre the Coccyx (See figure 2 on page 34)

This is not so easy to explain as so few of us have any concept of our coccyx. To align the coccyx correctly simply tuck in your buttocks not by thrusting them forwards but by rolling the pubic bone up slightly. This movement is only slight and therefore not much can be seen

other than a slight flattening of the lower back. The alignment of the lower spine is fundamental to correct posture within Tai Chi. An ache in your lower back after a short time probably means you are leaning back, which is incorrect.

SUMMARY

All of these considerations are the first steps to achieving proper posture and are required to do the form accurately. Once again I would remind you that this takes time to achieve so don't be disheartened if it does not all come together at once. Through regular practice these things will become second nature and after a while you will not need to think about them.

In Tai Chi Chuan we follow the Ten Essential Co-ordinations and avoid the Ten Deficiencies. For the Ten Essentials we need only know the first six as the last four are related to much higher principles than those covered in this book. As for the Ten Deficiencies nine of them are relevant and are listed accordingly.

SIX OF THE TEN ESSENTIAL CO-ORDINATIONS

1. The head co-ordinates with the coccyx
2. The neck co-ordinates with the waist
3. The shoulders co-ordinate with the inner thighs (known as the Kua pronounced K-wa)
4. The elbows co-ordinate with the knees
5. The shins co-ordinate with one another
6. The toes co-ordinate with one another

Each of these co-ordinations must work together at the same time. They take time to learn and will need revision and assessment on a regular basis.

NINE OF THE TEN DEFICIENCIES

1. The head is not suspended
2. The neck is not straight
3. The shoulders are not rounded
4. The elbows are not relaxed
5. The fingers are tense
6. The wrists are stiff
7. The body is not central
8. The legs are not bent
9. The chest and the coccyx are protuding

When practising your regular set of forms, pick one of the above points and note if you are doing it correctly.

Then in the following form try to ensure you have that aspect to the best of your ability. This way you begin to add these co-ordinations to your Tai Chi.

Footwork is of the utmost importance. If your feet are in the wrong position then you will not be solid on your feet.

Revise each of the postures of the form so that you are doing them as they are in the pictures, in the correct manner and direction.

Watching the movement of your hands will also help you focus as you practise.

Relaxation is not an easy aspect of the form to incorporate. This is because relaxation is much harder to develop than we think. It is useful to begin by telling yourself mentally to relax over and over again; this will help to develop a mindset that aims at relaxing the mind itself (see following chapter).

Don't train your form too fast. This is a huge error, although the speed can be variable when Tai Chi Chuan is practised properly. In spite of this, to practise too fast too soon can lead to errors in the form, giving you more to correct. Tai Chi Chuan is practised slowly to give you time to think about what you are doing and to have the opportunity to correct or add the principal needs of the form. The form should last about one and a half minutes to begin with and then should be slowed down so that eventually it can be done in approximately three minutes and, later, four minutes. Again, this will take time to achieve and will not happen overnight.

When practising the form it should be fluid. Like a flowing river, each movement reaches its zenith and cascades into the next one. If the form is jerky or stiff it is not being done at the correct speed for your skill level. You may also find yourself clipping the form; where some part of the movements, usually at the beginning or end of a section, are left out. If you keep doing this you will lose the form altogether.

Video is a useful tool in the practice of Tai Chi. By filming yourself doing the form and then analysing the play back you will see many faults in your performance. This might be a shock as we often have an image in our heads of what we look like as we do the form. Should you do this, always keep a note of the date as it will be useful to look back over your years of training and see your progress.

Allow yourself time to completely grasp and understand each new way of practising the form before you move on to the next aspect. Tai Chi Chuan is not an armchair art and no amount of theorising about the practice will enable you to do it any better. It takes lots of physical practice to improve and with this also comes a physical understanding that is then matched by a theoretical understanding. Repeating the form over and over is like reading a puzzle – the more you read the more faults and potential solutions become apparent.

This particular form uses a straight upright back most of the time. In some postures there is a slight rounding of the back but this is rare. A bent back inhibits the flow of Qi and blood and is at odds with the principles of Tai Chi Chuan. Some other styles interpret these principles differently and lean forward in some of their postures. Yet if you look more carefully you would see that the head is aligned with the spine. One thing is certain – leaning back or forth in any form is incorrect.

The biggest problem with leaning is the strain it puts on the back. Also bending forward or hunching causes our diaphragm to crush preventing correct breathing. Keep in mind the points raised earlier on the spine alignment and the postural considerations as they are designed to maintain good posture and good health.

Remember you are only as good as you are and there is no shame in that, whatever your skill level. There will always be people better and worse than you – be happy to be you.

"Keep an inner smile in your heart as much as possible, it helps to keep your spirits lifted and you can greet the world in a happier frame of mind".

Chapter Six
Training
Methods and Improving

This chapter explains how you should go about your daily or regular practice. It explains the best way to get the most from your routine training and guides you towards improving yourself.

It is important to train regularly in order to get the optimum benefits from any exercise and Tai Chi is no different. Ideally early mornings are the best time because once you have finished the rest of the day is free. However, since this form is so compact you will find it simply fits anywhere into your busy schedule as it can be practised anywhere.

If you work in an office you can fit in the Pa Tuan Chin during breaks away from the desk as it only takes five minutes to do. The exercises can replace some of the repetitive strain injury (R.S.I.) exercises that should be done at regular intervals. You can also find the time on a tea break to go through your form as it only takes a couple of minutes to complete. You could try practising whilst waiting for the kettle to boil. By adding a little daily training into your working life you are taking time out for yourself and when it comes to stress this is a good thing. When you do start doing these exercises at work you will find that you feel so much better for it.

Many people in South East Asia practise very early in the morning though this is probably because by 7.30–8.00am it is too hot to practise. Nonetheless if you want to practise in the morning, the Pa Tuan Chin is an excellent start to the day – after a cup of tea. By forming this good habit it will then take little effort to add the Chi Kung to the routine immediately following the Pa Tuan Chin.

Initially you should only do your Chi Kung for five minutes. You can then slowly build this up to the full fifteen minutes – never rush this either physically or mentally. Don't be too preoccupied with the length of your practice. After a while you will instinctively know how long five minutes is. Eventually you will be able to practise all three of the standing postures with ease.

As for the form, remember to firstly go through each of the preparation exercises, making sure that you stretch well and warm up correctly. Then practise your form at least three times. The following steps are recommended if you can only run through your form three times.

The first time: Your first run through is not going to be great. This is the way it always is; no matter how long you have been training.

The second time: Pick an aspect to concentrate on. e.g. correctness, posture, speed and look for inaccuracies in the aspect you have chosen.

The third time: You should do the form to the best of your ability and don't concern yourself over mistakes, just enjoy it this time around.

This is the least you should do most days. As the form takes such little time to run through you should easily find time to go through it many more times. In doing so you can really concentrate on particular aspects of the form and practise them repeatedly so as to improve many principles more quickly.

Speed is not a skill and in Tai Chi you should never practise the form in a rush. Practising a form quickly is something that should be done in Tai Chi Chuan but not at this time. Much more useful to you is the attainment of relaxation. Learning to relax will take some time to achieve. Just try telling anyone who is stressed to relax and the chances are that they will just get more stressed and angry. This is probably because in the modern world we have so many demands made upon our time that we are constantly thinking of what else we have to do. Also we have little in the way of mental training to calm our minds so like an unruly child, our minds run riot. The mind is like a raging sea, you can never pacify the waters completely but you can calm it down to gentle ripples. As time passes, through your practice, it will become easier.

One technique for calming the mind is to try counting in your mind picturing the number in your head.

Sit down somewhere quiet, resting back into a chair and let go mentally and physically as much as possible.

Breathe slow and deep via your nose and using your diaphragm.

Think of the number 1 and picture it in your head – and only the number 1.

Think of the number 2 and picture it in your head – and only the number 2.

Repeat this process for each number.

Each time you think of anything else start from the number 1 again. Be honest with yourself whilst doing this. If you can make it past the third number you are doing very well.

SUGGESTIONS FOR TRAINING

Wake up 15 minutes earlier than usual. Have a drink and then practise the Pa Tuan Chin – do this for one week before adding five minutes of Chi Kung

Whilst at work find an empty room, or use the roof if you have access,for your form practice. Take time out every couple of hours to run through it a few times. If you are not a smoker then you are merely taking the time allowed to others for smoking breaks. Besides which, the benefits to your well-being will probably make you more productive.

Without too much difficulty you should be able to fit in some training at certain points during the working day. Keeping this up on a regular basis will be very positive and in addition to this, the benefits of Tai Chi are cumulative, helping you to be healthier and happier.

Bear in mind you are learning an art and it takes time to perfect. As you have the rest of your life to practise there is no need to hurry. Take your time to get things right. Constantly reappraise your form to improve yourself. In no time at all you will be enjoying your practice and you'll miss it if you skip some out. Keep trying to overcome any difficulties you may encounter. Through repetition you will gain understanding and from there you will begin to see through the mists that cloud your eyes.

An extra bit of training that you might want to try out and that is fun to do is to practise the form in a swimming pool. It is not the easiest way to do the form but is good training and becomes so much easier once you have begun to understand the principles of Tai Chi and its movement. Once you have performed commencement, the water should be around you mid-chest level. From there continue with the form as normal. See how well you do. Repeat as many times as you wish, aiming to be as accurate and correct as possible each time. On the last go just do the form without a care in the world and enjoy it as much as possible.

"It is true that practice really does make perfect and can be fun too".

Chapter Seven
The Value of Sifu (teacher)

As a Sifu it has always seemed strange to me that so many students make the same mistakes as I did and had problems understanding the same points.

When I checked back with my teacher and training partner to see what their experience was, they were of a similar opinion. So a teacher's chief qualities are knowledge and an objective viewpoint.

Often they have faced many of the mistakes and problems that you will have to deal with and will be aware of common pitfalls.

It is difficult for us to be aware of:

- How our bottoms stick out whilst doing the form
- When our legs or arms are locked
- How our shoulders are tensed
- When our backs are hunched

A teacher will point these things out to you repeatedly until you notice them for yourself and correct them. By the time someone has reached the level of Sifu they should be able to do the form absolutely correctly both physically and on an internal level. They can combine all the principles into one long movement from start to finish. This is what you want to learn and this is what they should be aiming to teach you.

Traditionally the student teacher relationship is 'teacher says – student does' with little or no questioning. This approach is less common these days but nevertheless for a teacher and student there is a more important attitude to adopt. This is one where the correct way of thinking is 'do as I say not as I do'. The purpose of this is to lead the student through their training from the beginning, one step at a time.

Everyone wants to be able to just do things and if we can skip something in order to move on we try to. But in Tai Chi if you do that you never learn the foundations properly and eventually it will all come tumbling down. Start small and easy then work up. It is a bit like learning to juggle in that you begin with one ball and then two and so on. With Tai Chi you begin with one principle and once you have that you progress to the next until you can do them all together.

Your teacher should also be able to give you good health advice with tips on various cures for minor ailments you may suffer from. One gentle reminder I would like to point out is that your teachers are human and are as fallible as anyone else. Just as they need to be patient with you, you need to be patient with them. The best way to get the most out of your teacher is to practise. Here is where I can divulge a little secret known to all teachers and rarely to their students: it shows when you have practised and it is glaringly obvious when you haven't practised. You won't fool your teacher so don't fool yourself.

Any good teacher is not going to judge you on the amount of training you do – they will just accept what you can manage despite wanting you to train more. When they teach you something, it is your responsibility to practise it. This art is a progression and only when you have attained the step you are trying to get can you move to the one above. If you have not accomplished the level set before you then there is little point teaching you anything new. We all want to be taught something new so the best way to achieve this is to do as you are asked. That way your teacher will naturally reward you with more instruction.

Respect is not only given but also earned; by the student to the teacher and vice-versa. Traditionally respect has played an important part of training and it is still important today.

"Some people see it as a power so they don't teach but if many people do this then much is lost, it is better to give out all the information so that we can all grow".

Grandmaster Yu Yong Nian
Dachengchuanzhanzhuang

18th January 2006

Chapter Eight
Useful Health Tips

Traditional Chinese medicine has existed for at least 3000 years. It is not simply the use of needles and herbs but a culture and lifestyle that incorporates foods, teas, physical exercises and many forms of Chi Kung all designed to improve or maintain good health.

Slowly over the years we have had greater exposure to these strange ideas from the East. Now it is possible to find Chinese herbalists, acupuncturists and classes on Chinese arts in almost every high street. Anyone living near a Chinese community anywhere in the world can see them in the early mornings practising all manner of movements. Most of us look on slightly bemused yet intrigued.

These days there are a large number of Complementary and Alternative Medicine (CAM) therapies available to the general public, some of which have formed professional bodies that regulate them. These therapies have much to offer to the general public if they are used correctly and can be very useful in the treatment of many ailments. In my view these therapies should be complementary and not alternative. They may be alternative to western drugs but should be complementary to western medical treatments and not competitive. CAM therapists these days are better trained than ever before and often have a good understanding of western medical treatments and drugs.

For your own health it is often wise to consult your general practitioner (GP) before embarking upon a course of treatment of any kind. They may not display the kind of faith or attitude that you have but they should know if the treatment you wish to pursue will conflict with any existing treatments or known health problems. Your chosen therapist should also know of any potential conflicts of treatments.

We all get ill and/or injure ourselves, regardless of how strong we are physically or constitutionally, during the course of a lifetime. So it is handy to know a little of what makes you better or what would help in such situations. It is also unlikely that we will run off to the doctor with minor ailments like bruises, yet for the Chinese these require treatment like any other medical problem.

Though this may seem strange to those of us in the West, for the Chinese the reason is simple; in order for the body to be healthy it requires the free flow of Qi. Qi can't run freely if there is an injury or illness as these block up the energy pathways. This has a first line defence with the Pa Tuan Chin, which works in a preventative manner. As stated earlier, it clears the blockages from the meridians and strengthens the organs. Nevertheless accidents and illnesses happen and we do not need to suffer, we can treat a lot of these minor ailments ourselves.

The following suggestions are from years of experience and are remedies that can work well for the relevant complications. None of these suggestions will cause any harm, unless they are abused or you have some kind of allergy or hypersensitivity reaction. Unlike many Western medical treatments they do not have any side effects.

Diet

When it comes to diet and dieting, for the majority we are already aware of most of the do's and don'ts. In the case of diet in general we already know we should be eating a balanced diet. The question is just what is a balanced diet? Simply put, it is a reasonable daily allowance of proteins, carbohydrates and fats. The World Health Organisation has various pages on their website to give you further information if you are unsure about this.

The dieting industry bombards us all with information and images, designed to promote their products, usually every spring and summer. They can help to keep a reasonable level of nutrition whilst lowering calories and hopefully losing the desired amount of weight.

However, for many people once the diet is over it is not long before they start gaining weight again. There can be many reasons for this, not least of which is lifestyle and metabolism. As we get older our metabolism changes. It begins to slow down, and, combined with a less active lifestyle inevitably leads to weight gain. When losing weight we should try not to lose it too quickly. Instead we should adopt a new lifestyle that will help us to lose weight gradually and remain lost.

A very simple method of doing this is as follows; eat what you would normally eat but reduce your intake by one third, however increase your daily exercise by half, ensuring that you do some exercise that will make you sweat. When relating this to the exercises and Tai Chi form in this book I should point out that it is a common myth that Tai Chi does not work you hard or make you sweat.

Once you have tried the Chi Kung postures for five minutes you will know that they are also far more difficult than they look.

However, when attempting to lose weight in any large amount it is necessary to undertake more physical practice than is outlined here.

Swimming is an excellent form of exercise. Jogging is also very acceptable providing care is taken to use the right footwear and to run along not up and down as this just adds greater pressure to the knees, ankles and feet.

It is essential that food considerations and a sensible exercise programme are not only employed but also maintained. We forget that as children we were very active and as we grow up our lives become more sedentary. It is something that is to our detriment; it costs us our health. Remember prevention is cheaper than cure.

Another important point is that we, as human beings, are able to deal with being over weight relatively easily. Being overweight by a few stone can cause some problems but on the whole we are still well and able to behave as normal. However, being underweight by even a little is far more problematic and will begin to give us problems far quicker and easier.

Brandy Ointment

To begin with you need to prepare a mixture that you can use to help many ailments.

Strange as it sounds brandy is a useful rub. Similar to how an alcohol rub was used many years ago, but with the addition of ginseng it has more of an invigorating nature. Using a good bottle of brandy and a piece of ginseng root, preferably seven year old root, add the ginseng root to the brandy and leave for a couple of weeks. You

can shake the bottle everyday to mix it up a little. After this the brandy is ready for use. The ginseng will have infused into the brandy and this will give it a syrup- like texture. This mix can aid in the healing of damaged soft tissue. Apply this directly using your hands but do not apply to broken skin as it will sting. Using cotton wool will cause undue waste, as a lot of the mix will stay in the cotton wool.

Bruises

When you have a bruise, especially if it is a lump under the skin, you need to rub this hard to allow for the blood to flow for the healing to be fully effective. Firstly the body will have to break down the lump before it can fully heal the damaged area. You can aid this process by rubbing the area of the bruise immediately when the bruise appears. However this is not easy and is painful. An easier alternative is to sit in a hot bath or stand under a hot shower. Using soap to lubricate the skin, rub the area of the bruise hard in short bursts, running with the grain of the muscle. Do this for a little while, or for as long as you can handle it and the lump will reduce in size.

This will hurt but the pain will elicit a healing response and also limit the amount of rubbing you will do, thereby limiting the opportunity to over do. This will help improve the bruise and the blood circulation. After you have got out of the shower or bath and have dried off, use the brandy mix to spread over the bruise and it will heal much faster. Use the brandy mix everyday until the bruise is gone. For persistent bruises use the brandy morning and night.

Muscular Strains

With strains and sprains we need to get the blood moving through the area in order to get it to heal quicker. So it is back to the hot bath for another session of soapy massage. This time gently rub the area using the palm of your hand in a circular motion. Take it easy as, apart from being extremely painful, you only want to encourage the blood to flow through the tissue so that it can facilitate healing. Apply the brandy mix by hand to the swelling and damaged area. Repeat the brandy mix morning and night until the swelling has gone. Sprained ankles often hurt for some time after the swelling has gone. This is because the ligaments are still healing and will do so for a long time due to having an inherent poor blood supply.

Magnets

Small stick-on-magnets are now sold over the counter and these are very useful for helping injuries to heal. Placing them around the injury and leaving them on for a week before either re-sticking them or leaving them off having done their job. It is quite surprising how effective though subtle these little things can be. The stronger the magnetism (Gauss) the better. Do not throw them away as magnets do not lose their magnetism. You can keep them for future use.

Varicose Veins and Thread Veins

These can also be helped by the brandy mix as the combination of the alcohol and ginseng has a good effect on the enlarged veins. After using the brandy mix for a short amount of time you will notice a reduction in the size of the veins – don't stop.

Use the brandy mix regularly for a while to keep up the effect.

This mixture is not a cure all, but it can help with these minor ailments. Through my own personal experience, and that of my students and patients, I can say it works.

Strengthening the Ankles

To strengthen the ankles simply circle them in an outward turning motion; NEVER AN INWARD MOTION. This is most important as most sprains occur with the foot turning in on itself which stretches the ligaments on the outside of the ankle. Turning your foot inwards stretches and weakens the ligaments more, whilst turning outwards strengthens the muscle around the ankle as well as helping the blood to flow well in the area and so nourish the ligaments further. Repeat an equal number of times on both ankles, perhaps whilst you sit and watch the television.

Lo Han Kou

There is a nut called Lo Han Kou (pronounced Low Harn Co). This has great effect on the lungs and helps those suffering from respiratory problems including colds, sore throats and asthma. The seeds inside the nut can be boiled in water. When it is a rich brown it is ready to drink. Alternatively a ready prepared version is available in any Chinese supermarket. Follow the instructions within the packet as to how to prepare this drink. It recommends that you drink it three times a day but this is not necessary unless you are particularly ill. This seemingly innocuous drink has great effect though it is subtle in its action. It can be drunk by almost anyone (diabetics beware as it is very sweet) regardless of whether you are ill or not.

Sebaceous Cysts

Sebaceous cysts: (epidermoid cyst) a cavity in the skin connected to the surface by a pore, filled with skin debris and sebum, can be a problem and often the waiting list for their removal is a long one. So whilst waiting you have nothing to lose by trying this simple remedy.

Apply some calendula ointment once or twice a day to the cyst. Over a period of time, and this can be as little as weeks or as long as a few months, you should find that the cyst has reduced in size and perhaps even disappeared altogether. This is an old herbal remedy still used today by herbalists.

Pressure Points

Here are some common pressure points for some every-day conditions. Gently explore where these points are. The pressing of these points is always quick and short in duration so don't overdo it. The recipient will feel a sudden pain that is gone in seconds. Do not keep pressing but try to locate a point correctly and press once or twice.

The first condition to be dealt with is cramp, which is often a very uncomfortable and unpleasant experience.

Cramp in the thigh can be alleviated by a quick hard press with the thumb on to the point known as Feng Shi (Gall Bladder 31). This point is simply located by standing up straight and

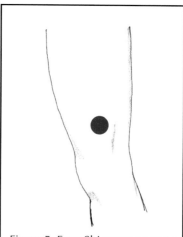

Figure 5. Feng Shi: press once or twice hard to remove cramp in the thigh.

placing your hands flat at the sides of your thighs. The point is located where the tip of your middle finger ends.

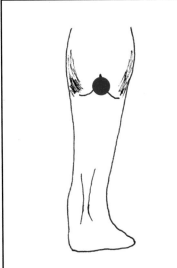

Figure 6. Cheng Shan: this point works excellently for cramp in the calf muscles. One short, sharp press of the thumb is enough.

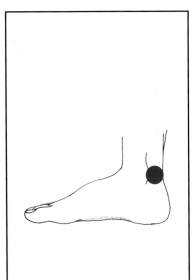

Figure 7. Taixi: a simple pinch using your finger and thumb will alleviate cramp in the foot.

Cramp in the calves is more common and very painful. For this use Cheng Shan (Urinary Bladder 57). Locate this point by standing on tiptoes. By doing this, the muscles of the calf splits into two, forming an inverted V.

The point is located at the head of this V shape.

Cramp in the foot is just as straightforward. Use the point called Taixi (Kidney 3) located in the tissue directly between the Achilles tendon and the mid point of the anklebone. Using a finger and thumb pinch the point. This will rid the cramp from the body of the foot. Cramp in the toes is more difficult to treat however by massaging the toes and the foot it will often release.

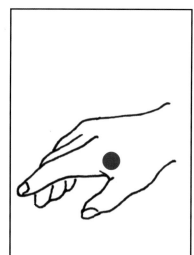

Figure 8. Hegu: useful for headaches and hiccups but should never be used on a pregnant woman.

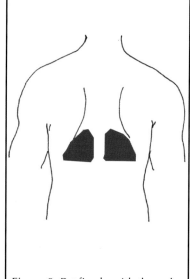

Figure 9. Pat firmly with the palm of your hand once or twice in the area shown but no lower.

Hiccoughs can usually be remedied by pressing on Hegu (Large Intestine 4). This point should NEVER be used on pregnant women. It is located between the thumb and index finger. Simply place the first crease of your thumb against the webbing of the opposite thumb and index finger. Then roll the thumb into the mid point of the hand index finger bone and squeeze. You will know when you get it right because it is painful like the others. This point is also useful for frontal headache but requires pressure of a sustained nature, so the key is to apply gentler pressure for a larger period of time.

Winding: When a person is winded it can be quite scary for them, especially if they can't get any breath at all. Help them by patting them on the back between the shoulder blades. Do this firmly but not so hard that you are knocking them over; this encourages the diaphragm to lower, enabling them to breathe again.

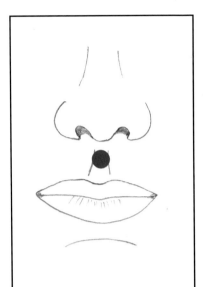

Figure 10. Renzhong: press this point with the knuckle of your index finger until the person starts coming around.

Fainting: If a person faints or becomes unconscious always call for medical help. If the cause is not serious you can usually bring them round by pressing the Renzhong point (Du 26). This is located in the centre of the upper lip between the lip and the septum of the nose. Use the knuckle of your index finger to press hard for a short burst.

Hypertension (High Blood Pressure)

Hypertension is a serious problem and is becoming more common of late. Regular exercise is a very good way to help deal with this and the exercises described in this book have a very good effect on maintaining a normal range of blood pressure. As doctors will tell you, avoiding high doses of sodium in your diet is a useful precaution to take.

An exercise that will help with hypertension is to sit down in a chair somewhere quiet. Close your eyes and focus your mind on the tip of each of your big toes. Do this for as long as you can. You should try to take five to fifteen minutes time for yourself in a tranquil space. Leaving the world behind you. It will still be there when you come back but you will be clearer in your mind and more relaxed in your body to enable you to deal with things better. This will not be easy at first but with time and practice it will become like the eye of a storm – a peaceful respite from the world.

Travelling

When travelling we are often sat in confined spaces for long periods of time. This is particularly the case on plane journeys.

Long periods of inactivity cause problems for the venous system, which relies on the action of the muscles in our bodies to push the blood back to the heart. It is important therefore to exercise what we can in these confined spaces. The ankle strengthening exercise is a good one to practise under these conditions. Another good exercise involves you using your toes; lift them towards you and then point them away in an alternate action. Additionally you can wriggle your toes, get up and walk about or lift your knees high for a few times. Drink water as opposed to alcohol as this can dehydrate you, lowering the amount of water in your blood and raising the chances of a deep vein thrombosis.

Massage

Massage is a great way to release tensions from the body and ease mental stress. This subject is really a topic in its own right. However, a few simple guidelines will enable you to give and receive a relaxing massage with good results and with little in the way of training.

Massage, as most people are aware, can be done by anybody. At some point we have all given a massage without really knowing what we are doing. On the whole this is fine as we rarely massage for long enough or hard enough to do any harm. So to keep things nice and simple – follow these pointers for a half body massage on the back.

TIPS

Ensure the lighting is soft so that no glaring lights are in your eyes.

The room should be warm as the recipient often feels cold as they relax.

When beginning to massage start at the base of the spine and work upwards.

Never dig with your fingers – use the pads of fingers, thumbs and hands.

Always follow the muscle.

Never flick over the muscle as this can tear the muscle fibres.

Mind, Body, Outlook

It is important to remember that there is always a mental aspect to illness, whether it be the hidden cause of the illness or the limiting factor to our recovery.

Yet it is also a vital part of our healing too. It is important to maintain a positive outlook as much as possible; sometimes it is useful to accept what it is your going through and this enables you to recover more quickly.

Stress is often (though not always) just another word for fear; fear of being late; fear of not doing your work on time or fear of upsetting others. Seeing stress for what it is can change your perspective on it and change its often negative effects on our health.

A little bit of tender loving care or just a little care goes a long way in today's society and this may be why so many people are turning to the complementary therapists who can spend time listening to their patients.

We all want to believe that we can be cured of our illnesses. This cure starts with us; it starts with how we deal mentally with our illness. A positive mental outlook or finding a psychological root can have very important effects upon our recovery rate.

Remember that we, as human beings live in three worlds all at the same time: a spiritual world, a physical world, a world of the mind.

The spiritual aspect is sadly lacking in our present day lives. Few of us focus on developing our spirituality and this is unfortunate. As for the physical world we all are far too preoccupied with our physical looks, needs and desires. Though important, the body is not everything. We need to look after not only our bodies but also our spirit and mind. The mind world is one that has, at times, too much focus on it yet at other times not enough. Balance is very important and we should try to balance our spiritual, physical and mental development.

Spiritual development does not inevitably rest in the hands of the world's religions. They offer their own methods towards spirituality but by no means are they the only methods and you should seek out the way that suits you best.

As for the psychological aspects of health, there are some very interesting and useful books available which may offer the reader an insight into ideas unveiling the possible psychological roots of illness. We should not forget that the mind is a powerful thing and can have dramatic effects on us both positively and negatively.

Another aspect of our lives that we often neglect is the element of fun. Laughter and happy feelings are quite possibly the best way to alleviate stress, as well as many other illnesses. Combine this fun with exercise and your endorphin levels will go through the roof, helping to combat stress and keeping you healthy all at the same time.

Finally, the Chinese say you should 'eat well, sleep well and do all things in moderation, then you will live a long healthy life'. This may be true but could also be a very boring one, so enjoy life, with all its ups and downs. Remember that it is when we overdo things and get rundown that opportunistic infections and diseases get their chance to thrive in our bodies, making us ill. Louis Pasteur, as he was dying remarked that it was the 'soil not the seed' that really mattered. So, looking after your mind, body and spiritual well-being helps keep the soil from allowing the seed to germinate.

"If an apple a day keeps the doctor away, then a smile a day keeps illness at bay".

Chapter Nine
Six Healing Songs

Song of the Lungs

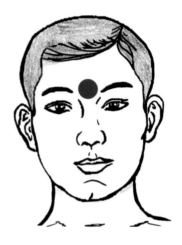

> *Organ*
> lungs i.e. the upper respiratory tract (which is made up of the nasal structures and the pharynx) and the lower respiratory tract (which is made up of the trachea, bronchi, bronchioles and alveoli).
> *Connected Organ*
> large intestine
> *Other Structures*
> sinuses and throat
> *Senses*
> none

Begin by sitting upright with your legs relaxed.

Rest your palms on your knees and breathe easily. Smile inwardly with your eyes closed and focus your mind on the area of the third eye. This is the mid forehead point.

Picture this as a mirror in which you can see the organs you are healing which are, in this case, the lungs and any of the associated organs, structures or senses.

When you feel relaxed bring the hands, palms facing inwards, to the mid-chest/bottom of the sternum, without touching the chest. Take a full deep relaxed breath and as you breathe in visualise the air coming in as a cool blue, filling all the structures you want to strengthen. Then, as you finish your inwards breath, picture this air heating up and turning a red colour. This is what you are about to breathe out like fire from a dragon.

Keeping the teeth gently closed, draw apart the corners of the mouth and raise your hands above your head. Rotate the palms round and upwards as they are pushed with palms facing upwards. Tilt the head back to look through your hands as they push to the sky and breathe out in a long relaxed breath through your teeth, whilst making the sound 'SSSSSSS'. Remember that the sound for all the songs is made in your head and not audibly.

At the same time inwardly watch the hot energy as it is drawn up in the breath, caught up in the sound and expelled out through the mouth as you breathe out fully. Then relax your arms whilst breathing in gently. Continue to relax as you breathe gently for four to eight breaths. Continue to smile inwardly and repeat this eight times.

It is a useful idea to clench the pelvic floor muscles whilst breathing out to allow the free flow of energy.

Song of the Kidneys

Organ
kidney.
Connected Organ
bladder
Other Structures
Urino-genital tract
Senses
sex organs, ears

Commence by sitting upright with legs relaxed. Rest your palms on your knees and breathe easily. Smile inwardly with your eyes closed and focus your mind on the area of the third eye.

When you feel relaxed bring the legs together and the hands together around the knees. Interlock the fingers so that they hold the legs together as you take a deep, relaxed breath. In your third eye mirror imagine the cool, blue air coming in down to the organs of the kidney, bladder, prostate, and sex organs. See the air turning hot and red and be ready to breathe it out like fire, as before.

Simultaneously pull back with the hands and breathe out. While contracting the abdomen to create pressure on the kidneys from the inside, purse your lips into a small O shape and make the sound 'WOOOOOOO', in your mind.

Repeat the relaxation as before and then repeat this exercise eight times.

Song of the Liver

Organ
liver
Connected Organ
gall bladder
Other Structures
ligaments and tendons
Senses
eyes

Begin in the same way as before but this time look to the liver and gall bladder in the third eye mirror. When you feel relaxed breathe in deeply and bring your hands up above your head. Clasp fingers with palms facing upwards and tilt your head back gently. Visualise the air flowing as in the previous exercises.

Make an open kiss shape with your lips. Push your hands up in a big stretch, with emphasis on the right side so that you lean slightly to the left. As you do so, breath out, making the sound 'SHHHHHHH', in your mind. At the same time watch the hot energy leaving the areas you have focused on, breathing out the fire of stagnant energy.

Then relax, as before, breathing gently and repeat eight times.

Song of the Heart

Organ
heart
Connected Organ
small intestine
Other Structures
pericardium, arteries and veins
Senses
tongue

The start of this exercise is the same as for the lungs and is so for all but one of the six healing songs. Visualise the heart and its connected organs in the mirror point. Take a deep, relaxed breath, making a round shape with the mouth. Lift your hands above your head as you did with the Liver song but this time extend your stretch on the left-hand side leaning over slightly to the right. As you breath out make the sound 'HAWWWWW', in your head.

Remember to use the visualisation technique as before but substituting the lungs and liver for the heart. Watch the hot energy leaving and on the in-breath see the clear energy entering. Repeat as with the previous exercises.

Song of the Spleen

Organ spleen *Connected Organ* stomach *Other Structures* pancreas *Conditions* digestion problems, lack of concentration (this may help ulcers to some extent)

Once again we start by picturing the organs; this time the spleen and its associates in the mirror point. When you feel relaxed bring your hands up to the mid-chest area, placing your middle and your index fingers at the bottom of the sternum, slightly to the left.

Take a deep, relaxed breath and make a small round O as before but not as small as for the Song of the Kidneys. As you breathe out, make the sound 'HHHOOOO', in your mind whilst gently pressing in with your fingers. Once you have finished breathing out relax as before and repeat eight times.

Song of the Sanjiao

Organ sanjiao (three chambers of the torso) *Connected Organ* in Chinese meridians this links with the pericardium *Other Structures* Qi of the torso *Senses* blood and Qi circulation *Avoid* vibrations, cold and drafts

When practising all of the songs always do this one last.

Commence by lying down; this can be done when you go to bed before sleeping. Should you sleep before completing the eight rounds that is fine. Rest yourself and breathe easily.

Smile inwardly with your eyes closed and focus your mind on the area of the third eye. Focus on the whole of the torso, viewing it from the base of the neck to the perineum. Also picture it from the inside and outside respectively.

When you feel relaxed take a deep breath. Take a full breath filling the upper chamber of the chest first, then letting that spill over to the middle chamber and then to the third, lower chamber, until you can't breathe in anymore.

Picture (in your third eye) the air warming up turning from a cool, blue to a hot, red colour. Smile a big smile (grinning with teeth on show) and breathe out making the sound 'HEEEEEEE' in your mind. Breathe out in a long action, emptying from the lowest chamber to the upper chamber in a reverse action of breathing in.

Once completely out of air breathe in and relax for a few breaths. Picture a white light filling your entire torso as you gently breathe in and out before beginning the cycle again. Repeat until you have finished eight breaths.

Practise this every night before going to sleep.

Acknowledgements

This book is based on the knowledge I gained at the instruction of My Sifu and my thanks goes out to him for the many years of patient teaching, the countless gentle reminders of 'bend your legs' along with many others, and oh yes the even more countless bruises. Thankfully he also taught me how to treat them too.

I would also like to thank Grandmaster Yu Yong Nian for accepting me as his student and teaching me with great humility and skill, I have never met a man quite like him and it is a great honour for me to train with him. My thanks also go to my Tai Chi brother Douglas Robertson, my worthy opponent and brother in arms. Without his relentless striving to get the better of me I would not have had the equal drive to do the same and, in so doing, drive each other on to finally reach the rank of Sifu ourselves.

Over the years we have fought, trained, argued, trained, laughed and trained some more and when the frustration and pain of training brought us to the edge of tears we were there for each other with a comforting word and a helping hand back up onto our feet to start over again. As the first serious students of our Sifu we have trail blazed a path for those students who have followed us. And we now have stories of our own training to tell, of how we found it tough yet managed to persevere, as we help them to do the same.

It is through our students that we truly show what it is we know, for it is not enough that we "can do" this art but that we have students who "can do" also. Only through our teaching of the whole art can we keep safe its traditions, its history, its skills, its benefits (martial and health) and therefore, its future.

My thanks go to the models for their help with this book: Matthew Calvert, Daniele Buccheri and Tina Andersen. A word of thanks must also go to my family; Janet, Susan, Moira, Trish, and Alison, Alan, Andy and their families and also to my cousins, Yvonne, Jeanette and Rod, as well as to my friends; Deniz, Helen, Paul, Narita, Neil, Helen, Sam, Karl, Carol, Emma, Julie, Doug and Sandy to name but a few. All of whom have shown me such amazing love and support especially in recent times and without such wonderful people where would any of us be. My gratitude also goes to Doug whose input is always appreciated and to Deniz for the editing of this work and for all his efforts at keeping me on the path of good English, which is no mean feat.

And lastly my thanks to Trefor Ball for his help with the photographic studio and its set up and to Damon Smith and Jeremy Mills at Jeremy Mills Publishing for having faith in this book enough to publish it.